It's Easy To Play Paul Simon

Wise Publications
London/New York/Sydney

Music Sales Limited
8/9 Frith Street, London, W1V 5TZ, England.

Music Sales Pty. Limited
120 Rothschild Avenue, Rosebery, NSW 2018, Australia.

ISBN 0.86001.421.5
PS 10214
Arranged Cyril Watters

Printed in England by
Eyre & Spottiswoode Limited, London and Margate.

Still Crazy After All These Years

Words and Music by Paul Simon

years.
Oh, still
cra- zy
af - ter
all
these
years.
Em
C♯dim
G
D7
Cm
1
D7
G
C
G
2. I'm not the
2
years.
G7
mf
Four
in the
morn - ing,
crapped out,
yawn-ing,
long - ing my
life
a-
A maj 7
A
E
Em
G♯m
C
-way.
I'll
nev - er
wor - ry;
why should
I?
F♯
Em7
B
C
B
C
G
It's
all
gon - na
fade.
G7
C
B
C
B
C

Now I sit by my win-dow and I watch the cars;
B Am7 G G7 C
I fear I'll do some dam-age one fine day. But I
F7 G F♯dim B D7
would not be con-vict-ed by a ju-ry of my peers. Still cra-zy aft-er
G G7 C C♯dim G
all these years; Oh, still cra-zy, still
D7 D♯dim Em C♯dim G
f
ritard.
cra-zy, still cra-zy aft-er all these years.
C F C7 G D7 G C G

50 Ways To Leave Your Lover

Words and Music by Paul Simon

hab - it to in - trude; I hope my mean-ing won't be lost or mis - con - strued. But
sleep on it to - night; I'm sure in the morn-ing you'll be - gin to see the light." And then she
C B Em C dim B7
I'll re - peat my-self at the risk of be-ing crude.
kissed me and I re - al - ised she prob - ab - ly was right.
There must be fif - ty ways to leave your
Em D C Em Am
lov - er, fif - ty ways to leave your lov - er. Just slip out the
Em Am Em
back, Jack; make a new plan, Stan; you don't need to be coy, Roy;
just get your-self free.
just lis - ten to me.
G Bb C7
Hop on the bus, Gus; you don't need to dis - cuss much; just slip off the
G Bb
key, Lee, and get yourself free. Slip out the free.
C7 G G
Last time to Coda
D.S. al Coda (with repeats)
CODA
free.
G

My Little Town

Words and Music by Paul Simon

school; rid - ing my bike past the gates of the fac - tor - ies;
Em Gm C7 F
My mom do - ing the laun - dry, hang-ing our
D7 Eb7 Ab Eb Eb+
shirts in the dir - ty breeze. And af - ter it
G7 C
rains there's a rain - bow, and all of the col - ours are
F G7
black. It's not that the col - ours aren't there; it's just im-ag - i -
C Dm C

3
-na - tion they lack. Ev - 'ry - thing's the same
F C D Dm7
back in my lit-tle town.
G7 C
mf No-thing but the dead and dy - ing, back in my lit - tle town,
C Bm7 Am
No-thing but the dead and dy- ing, back in my lit - tle town.
C Bm7 Am
In my lit-tle town, I nev-er meant no-thing, I was just my
G Em7 Gm C7

fa - ther's son.
Mm.
Sa - ving my
F
D7
Eb
Ab
mon - ey,
dream - ing of
glo - ry;
Twitch-ing like a
Eb
Ab
Eb
Ab
fin - ger on the
trig - ger of a
gun!
Leav - ing
Eb
Eb+
C
mf
no-thing but the dead and
dy - ing, back in my lit - tle
town.
C
Bm7
Am
No-thing but the dead and
dy - ing, back in my lit - tle
town
Repeat and fade
C
Bm7
Am

I Am A Rock

Words and Music by Paul Simon

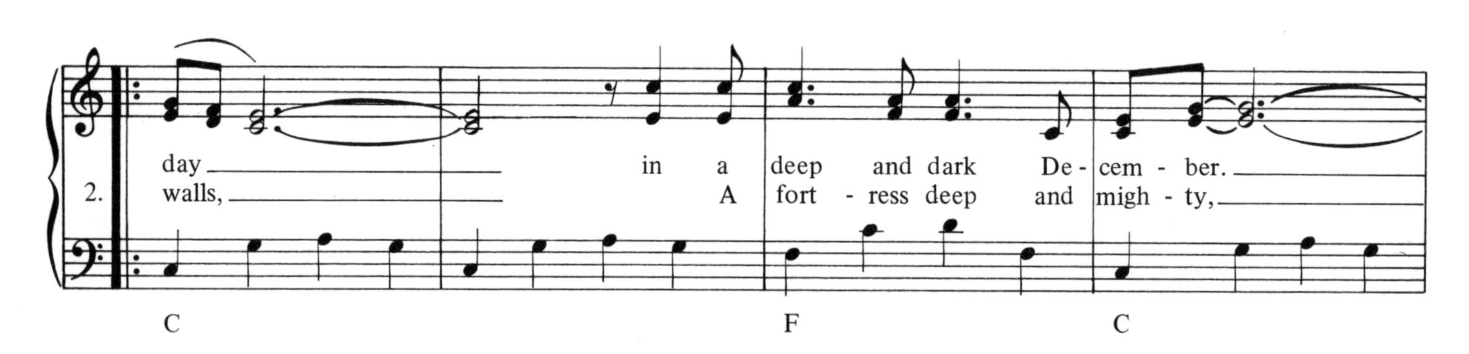

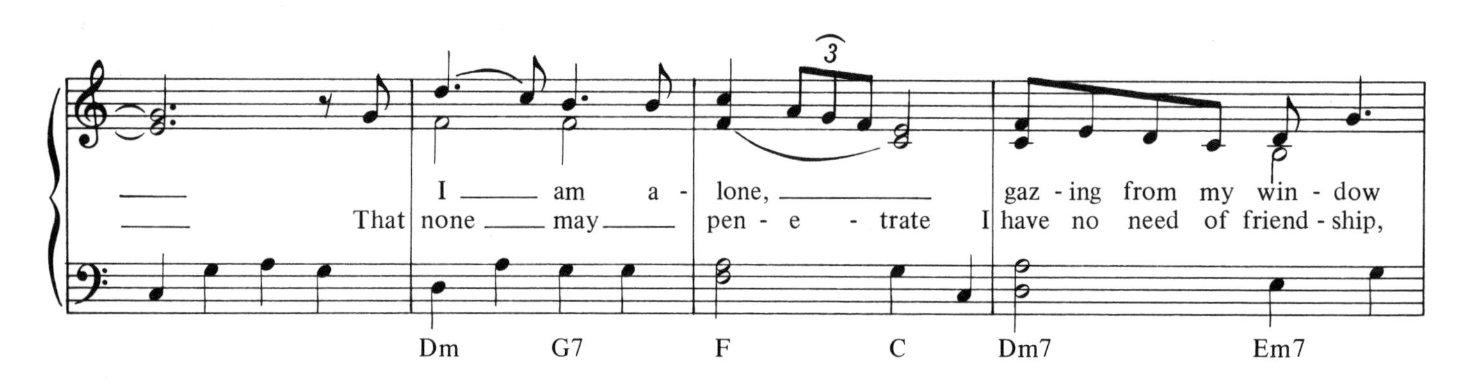

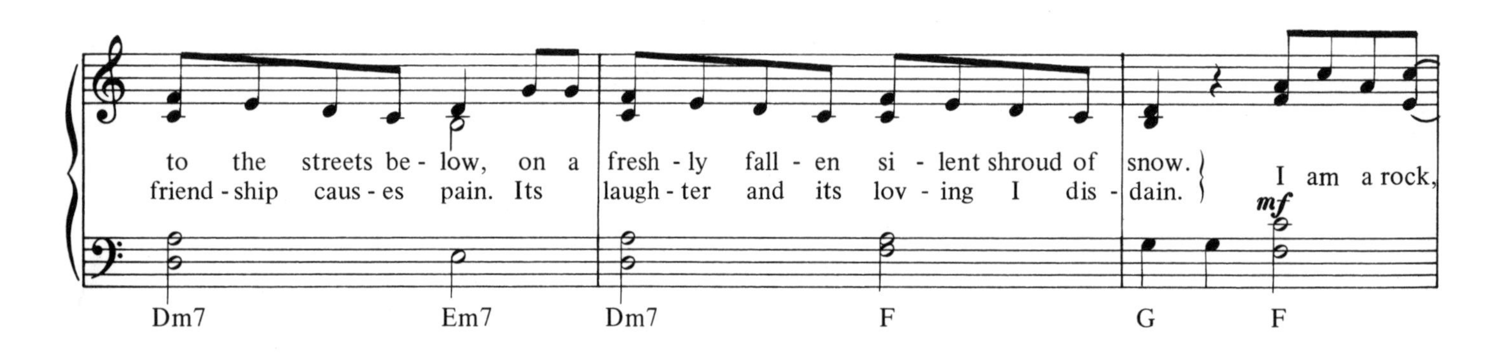

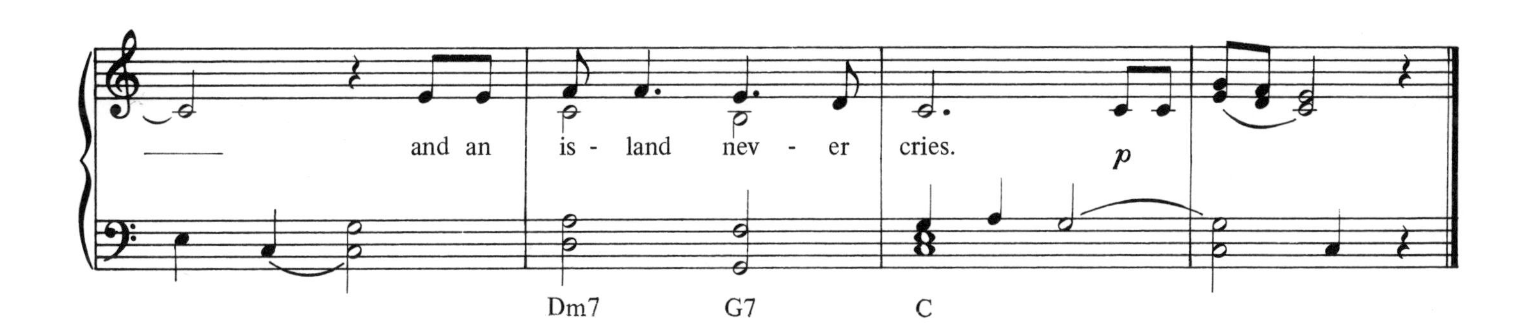

3. Don't talk of love, but I've heard the word before;
   It's sleeping in my memory.
   I won't disturb the slumber of feelings that have died.
   If I never loved I never would have cried.
   I am a rock, I am an island.

4. I have my books and my poetry to protect me,
   I am shielded in my armour.
   Hiding in my room, safe within my womb,
   I touch no one and no one touches me.
   I am a rock, I am an island.

Homeward Bound

Words and Music by Paul Simon

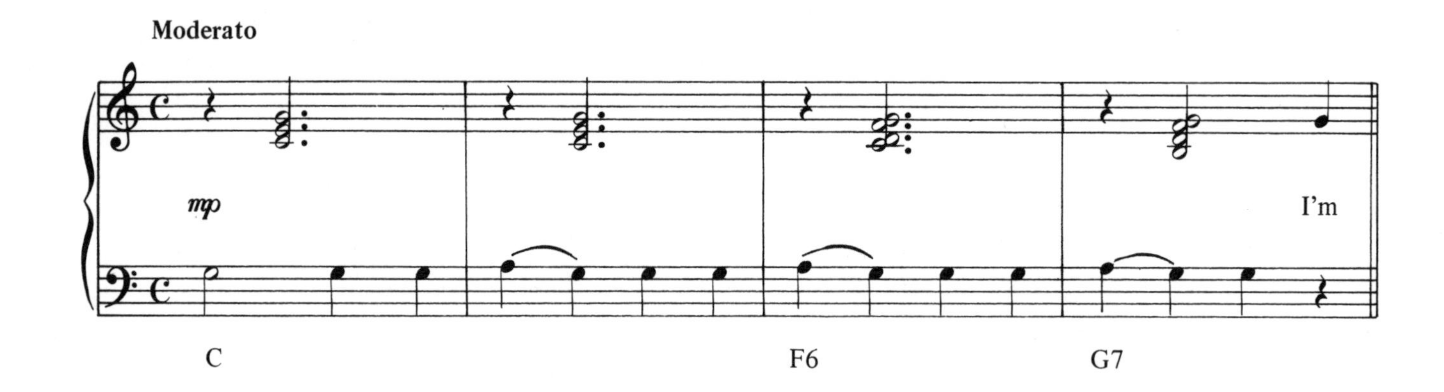

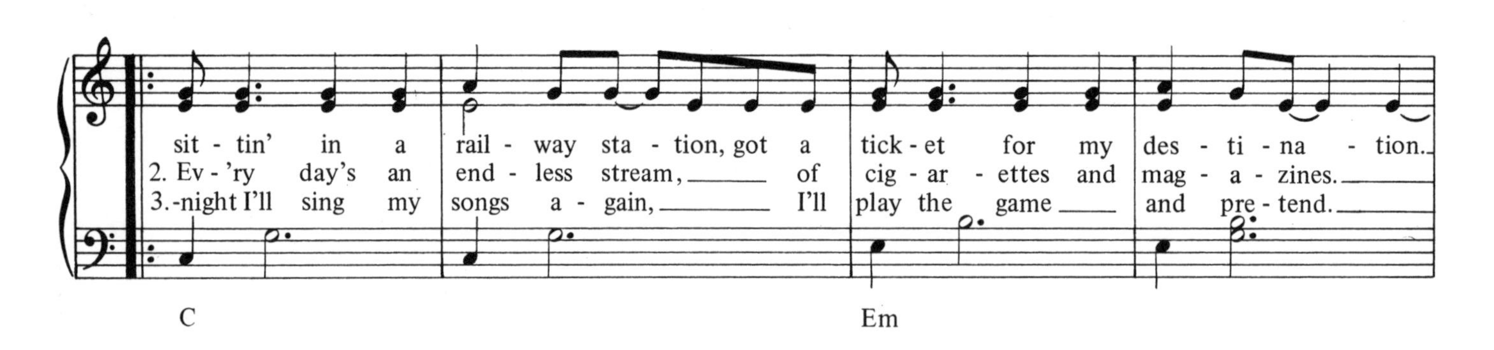

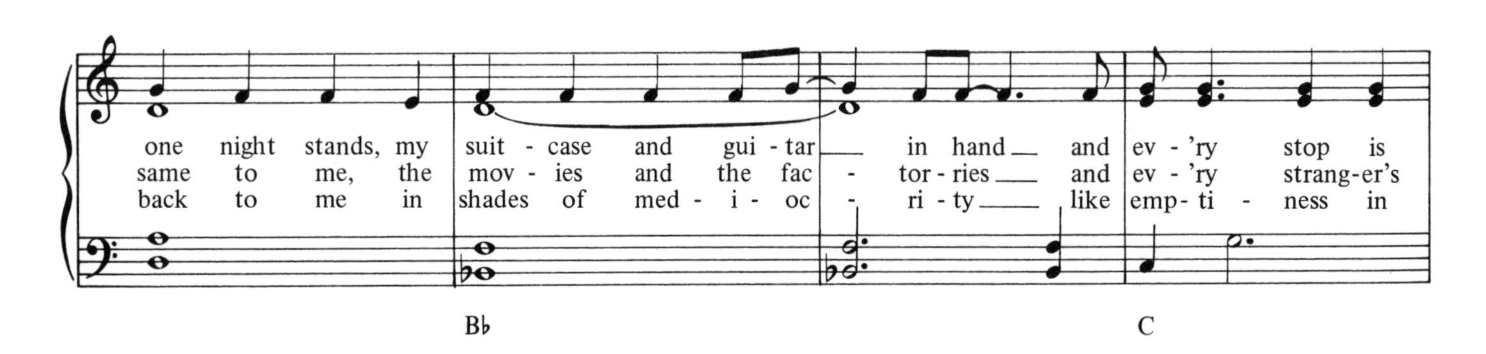

neat - ly planned for a po - et and a one - man band.
face I see re - minds me that I long to be.
har - mo - ny I need some - one to com - fort me.

CHORUS
Home - ward bound, I wish I was, Home - ward bound.
C F C F

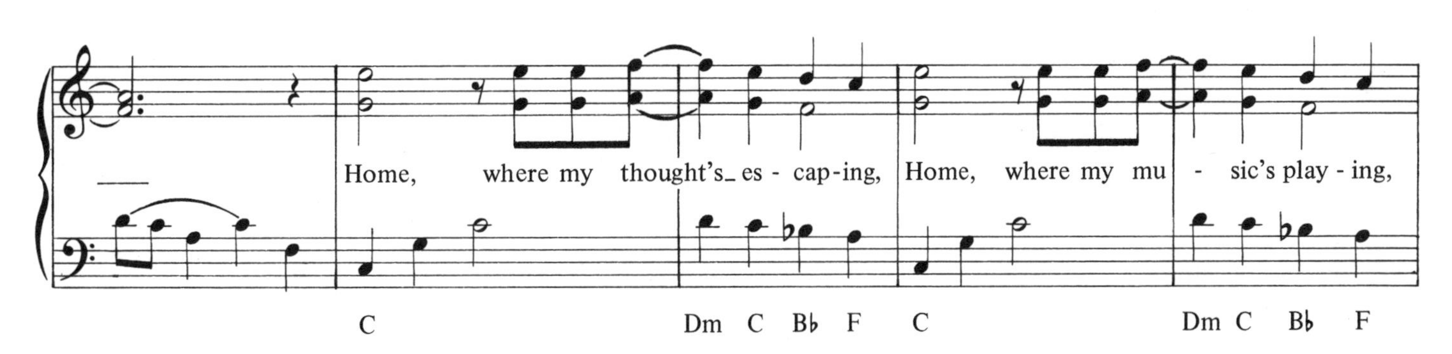
Home, where my thought's es - cap-ing, Home, where my mu - sic's play - ing,
C Dm C B♭ F C Dm C B♭ F

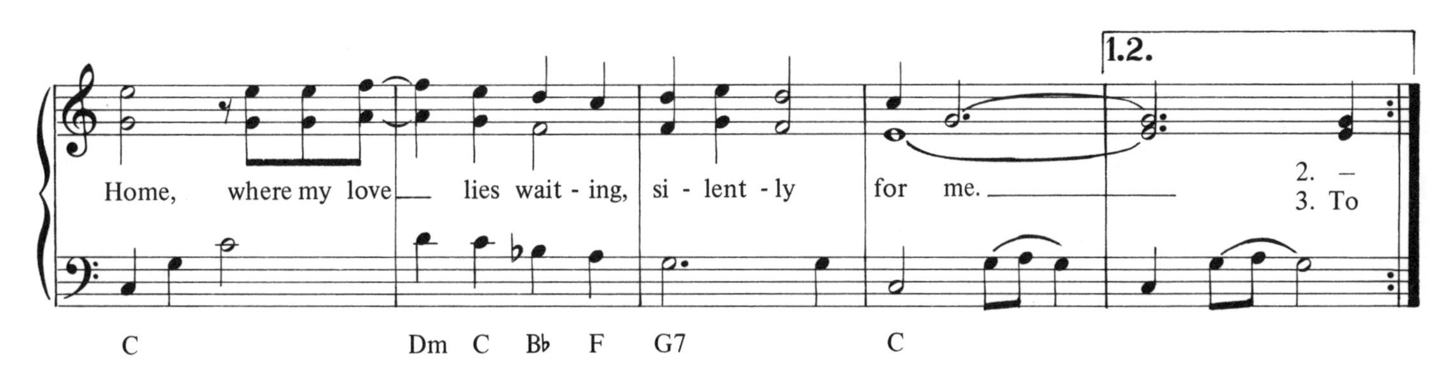
1.2.
Home, where my love lies wait - ing, si - lent - ly for me.
2. –
3. To
C Dm C B♭ F G7 C

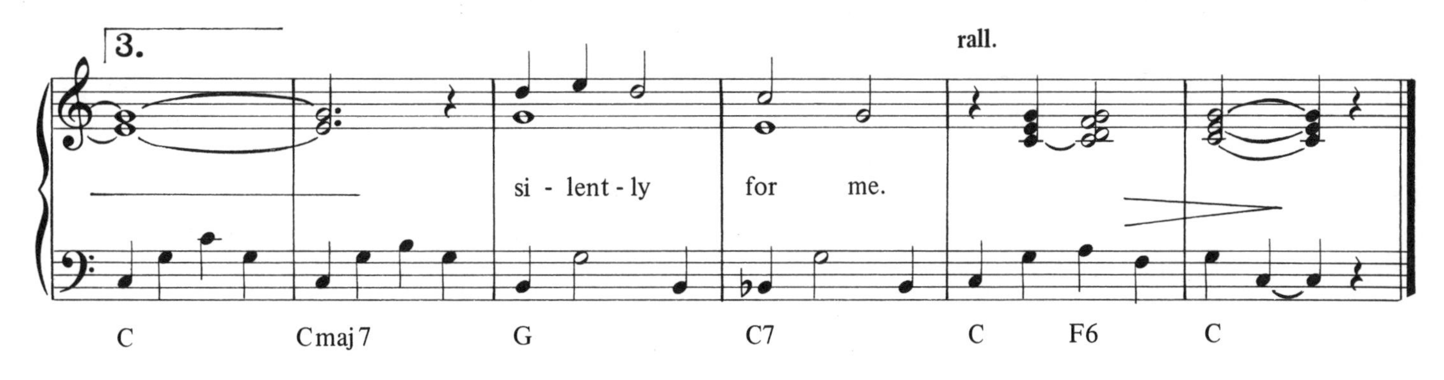
3.
rall.
si - lent - ly for me.
C Cmaj7 G C7 C F6 C

El Condor Pasa

English Lyric by Paul Simon
Musical Arrangement by J Milchberg, D Robles

man gets tied up to the ground, He gives the world it's sad-dest sound, it's sad-dest
C
G
sound.
I'd ra-ther be a for-est than a
Em
street. Yes I would, if I could, I sure-ly would. I'd
G
Em
ra-ther feel the earth be-neath my feet. Yes I would, if I on-ly could, I sure-ly
3
G
would.
Em
C
G
rall.
C
G
Em

Scarborough Fair

Arrangements and Original Counter Melody by
Paul Simon and Art Garfunkel

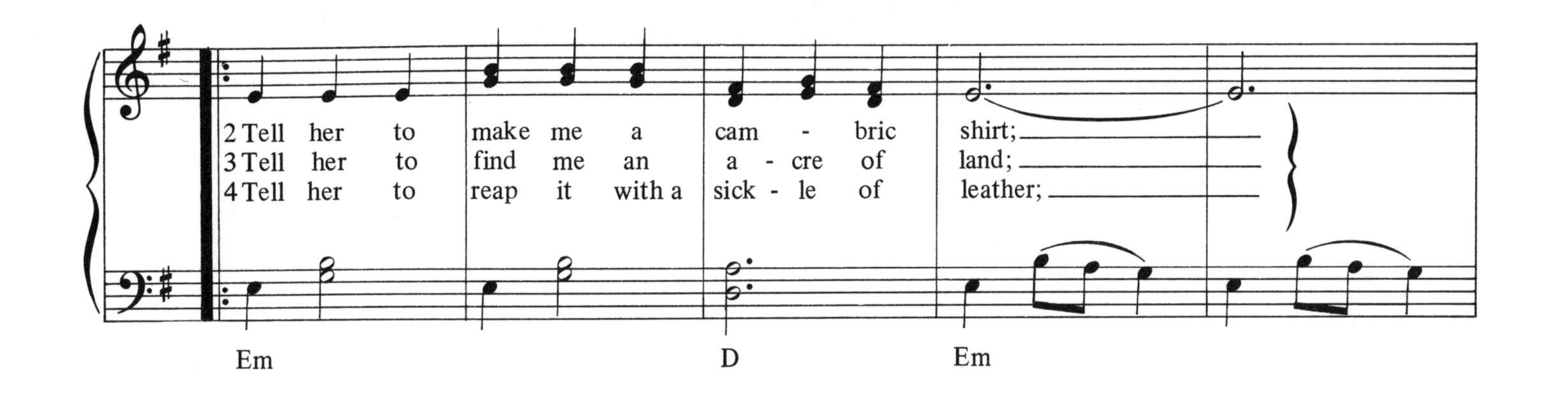
2 Tell her to make me a cam - bric shirt;
3 Tell her to find me an a - cre of land;
4 Tell her to reap it with a sick - le of leather;
Em D Em

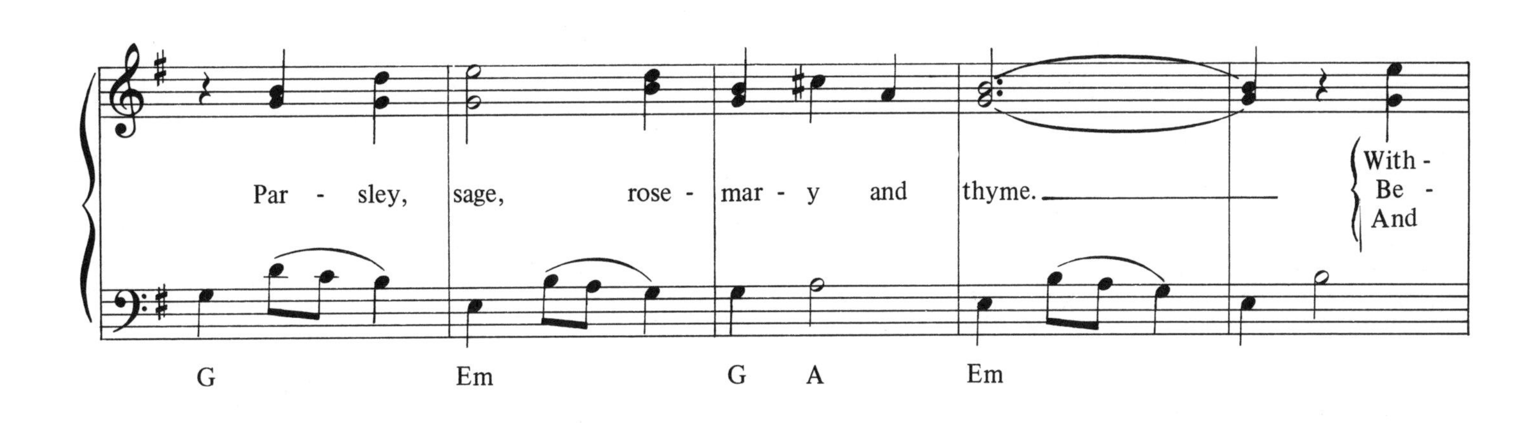
Par - sley, sage, rose - mar - y and thyme.
With -
Be -
And
G Em G A Em

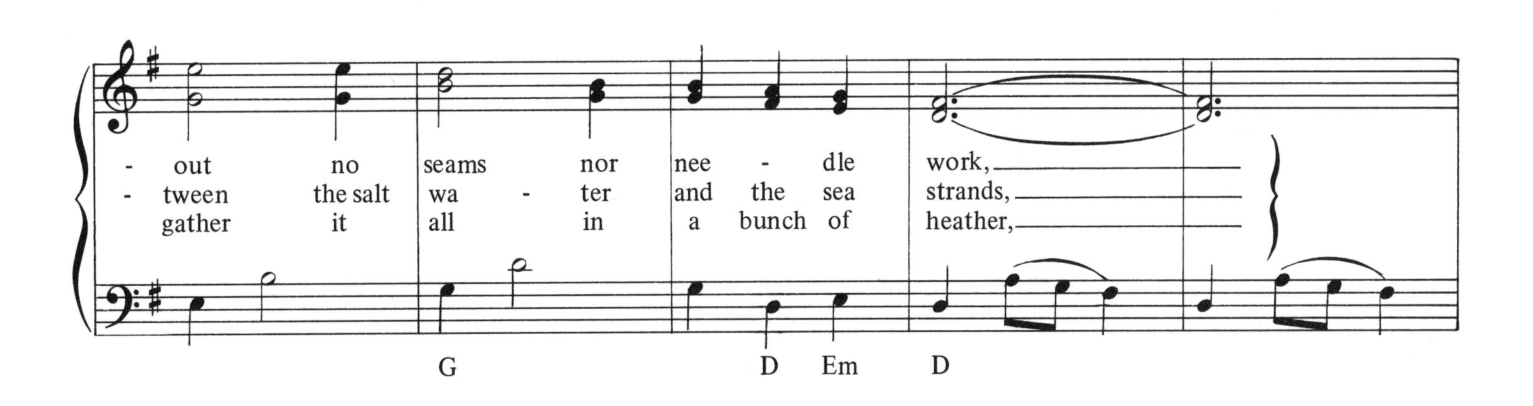
- out no seams nor nee - dle work,
- tween the salt wa - ter and the sea strands,
gather it all in a bunch of heather,
G D Em D

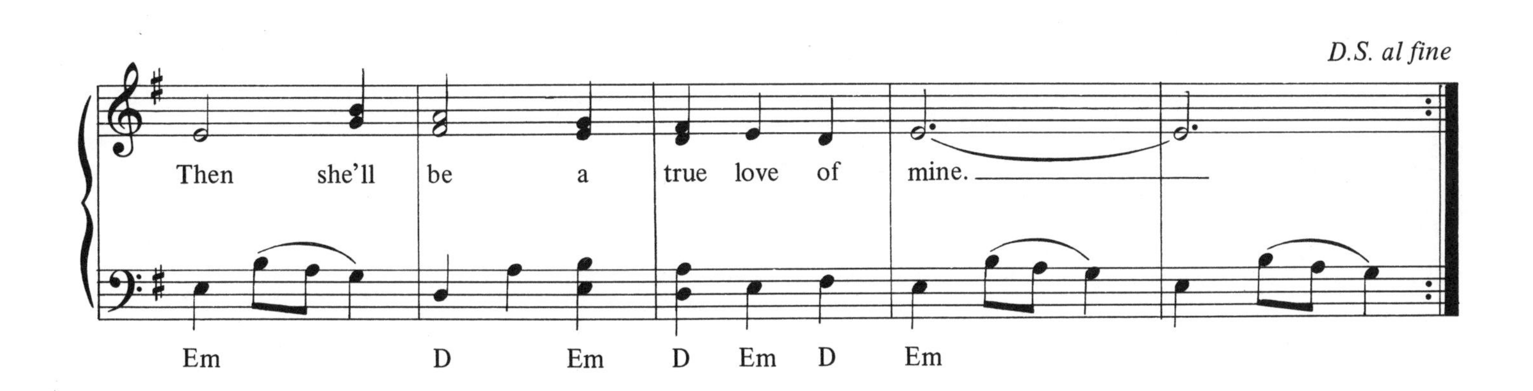
D.S. al fine
Then she'll be a true love of mine.
Em D Em D Em D Em

Mrs Robinson

Words and Music by Paul Simon

VERSE
like to know a lit - tle bit a - bout you for our files.
A7 D A Em7 A7
We'd like to help you learn to help your -
D A7 D
self.
Look a - round you, all you see are
D9 G Dm C
sym - path - et - ic eyes.
Stroll a - round
F Dm A
D. S. al Coda
the grounds un - til you feel at home. And here's to
G A G

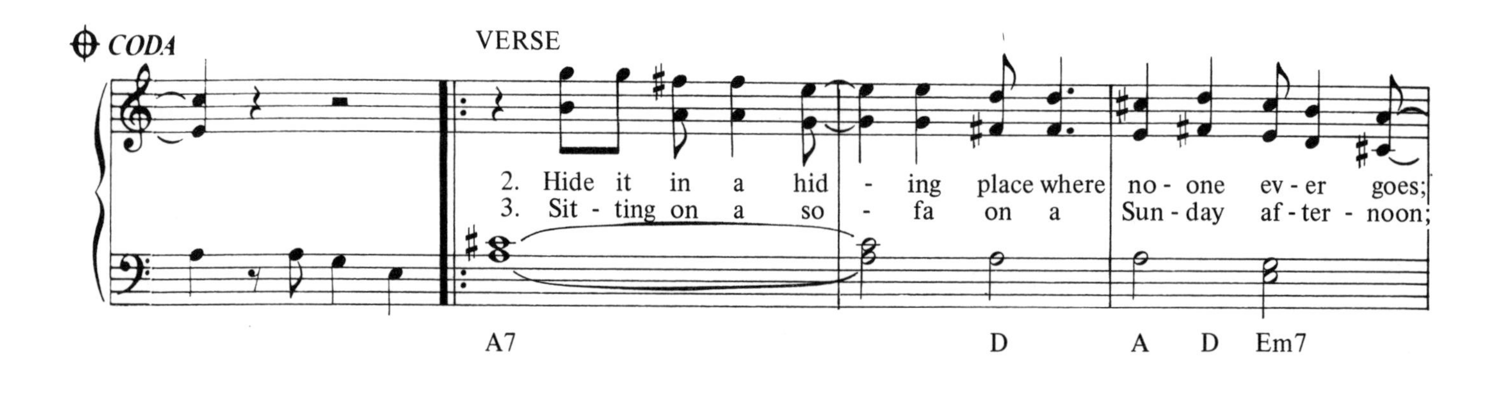
CODA
VERSE
2. Hide it in a hid - ing place where no - one ev - er goes;
3. Sit - ting on a so - fa on a Sun - day af - ter - noon;
A7 D A D Em7

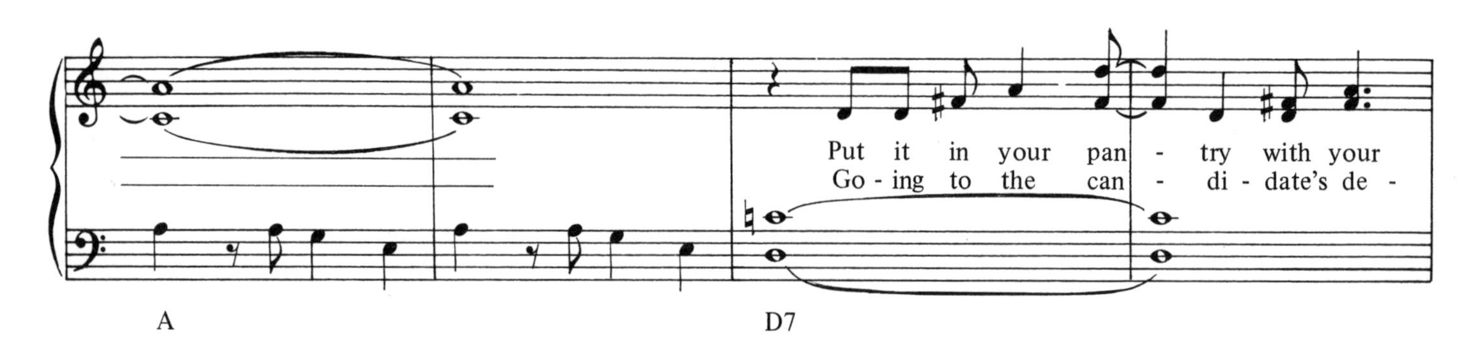
Put it in your pan - try with your
Go - ing to the can - di - date's de -
A D7

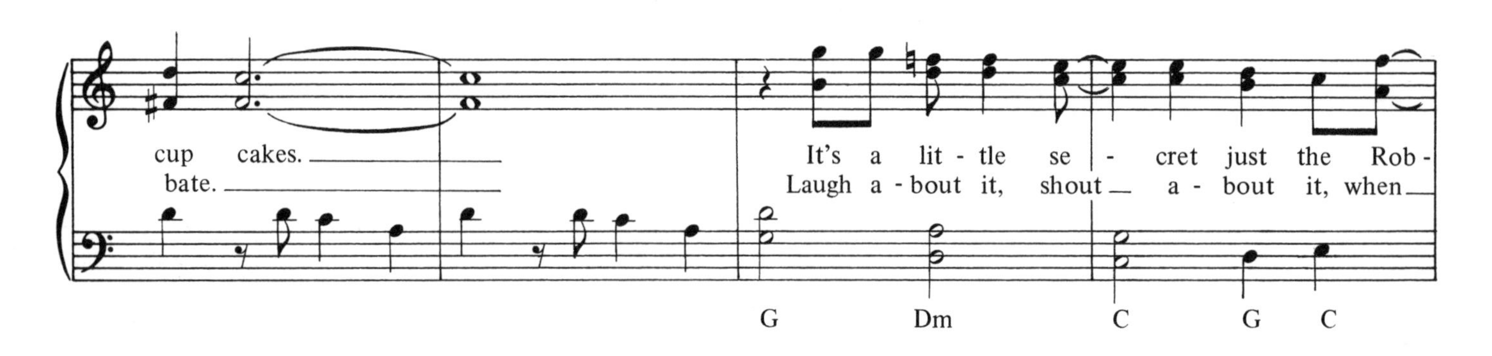
cup cakes. It's a lit - tle se - cret just the Rob -
bate. Laugh a - bout it, shout a - bout it, when
G Dm C G C

- in - son's af - fair. Most of all
you've got to choose. Ev'ry way you look
F Dm A

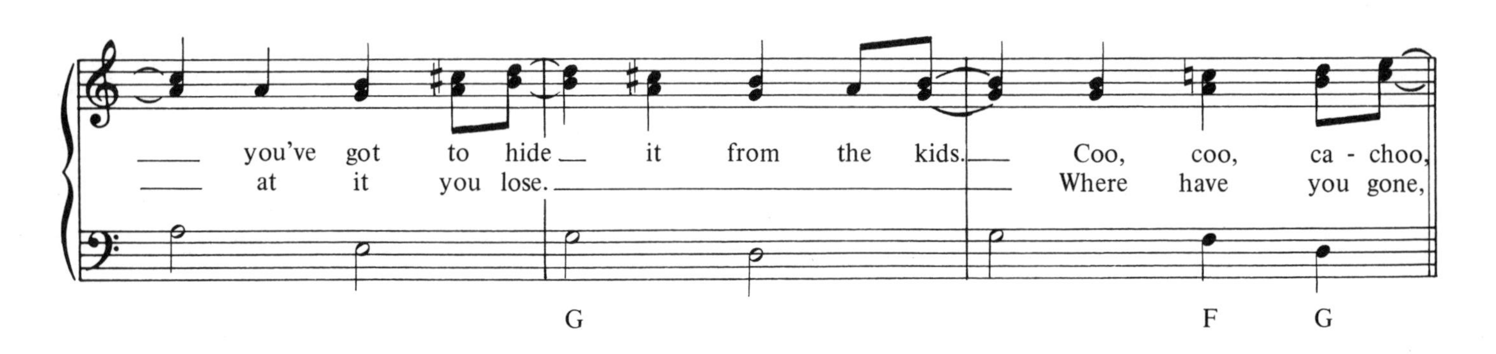
you've got to hide it from the kids. Coo, coo, ca - choo,
at it you lose. Where have you gone,
G F G

CHORUS
Mrs Rob - in - son, Je - sus loves you more than you will
Joe Di - mag - gi - o? A na - tion turns its lone - ly eyes to
C
Am
C
Am
know, (Wo, wo, wo) God bless you
you, (Woo, woo, woo) What's that you
F
Dm7
G7
please, Mrs Rob - in - son, Hea - ven holds a place for those who
say, Mrs Rob - in - son, "Jolt - in' Joe has left and gone a -
C
Am
C
Am
pray. (Hey, hey, hey, Hey, hey, hey.
way. (Hey, hey, hey, Hey, hey, hey.
F
Dm7
Dm
1
2
)
)
A
A

The Sound Of Silence

Words and Music by Paul Simon

Fairly slowly

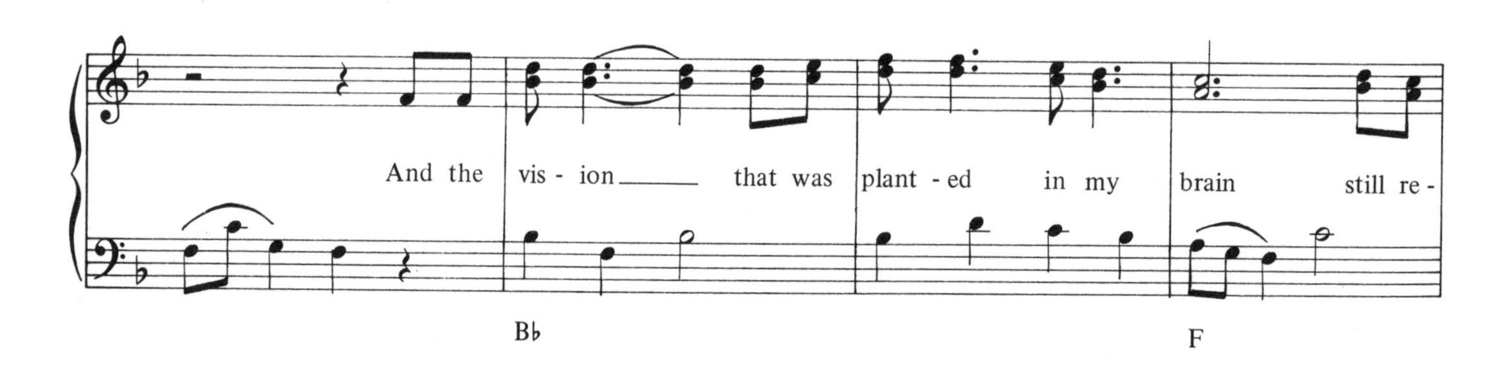

- mains with - in the sound of si - lence.
Dm F C7 Dm
2. In rest - less dreams I walked a - lone, nar - row streets of cob - ble - stone, 'Neath the ha - lo of a street - lamp, I turned my col - lar to the cold and damp. When my eyes were stabbed by the flash of a ne - on light that split the
3. And in the nak - ed light I saw ten thou - sand peo - ple, may - be more. Peo - ple talk - ing with - out speak - ing, peo - ple hear - ing with - out list - en - ing. Peo - ple writ - ing songs that voi - ces nev - er share and no one
Dm C Dm F B♭ F B♭ F B♭ F

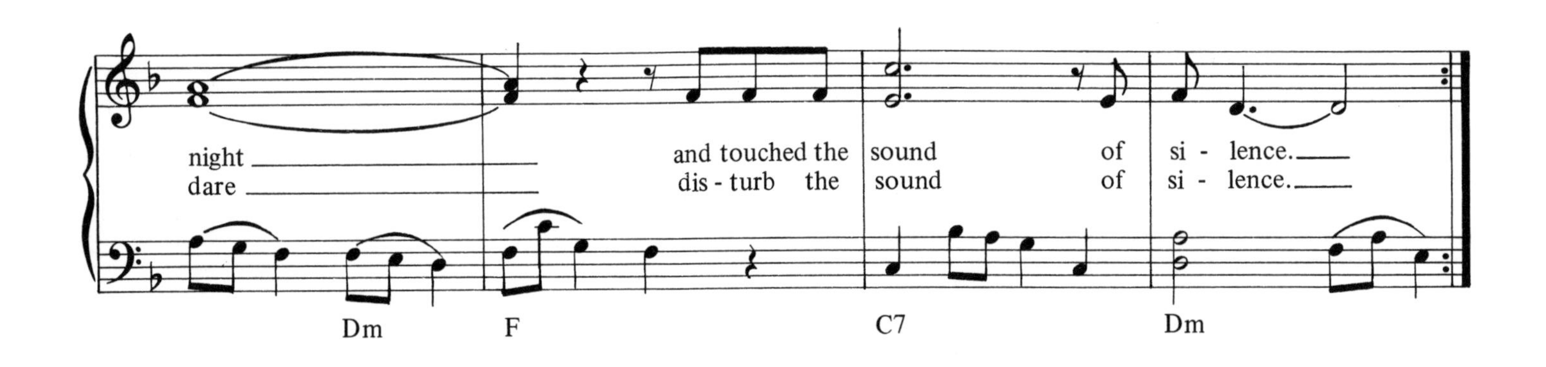
night and touched the sound of si - lence.
dare dis - turb the sound of si - lence.
Dm F C7 Dm

4. "Fools!" said I, "you do not know, si - lence like a can-cer grows."
C Dm

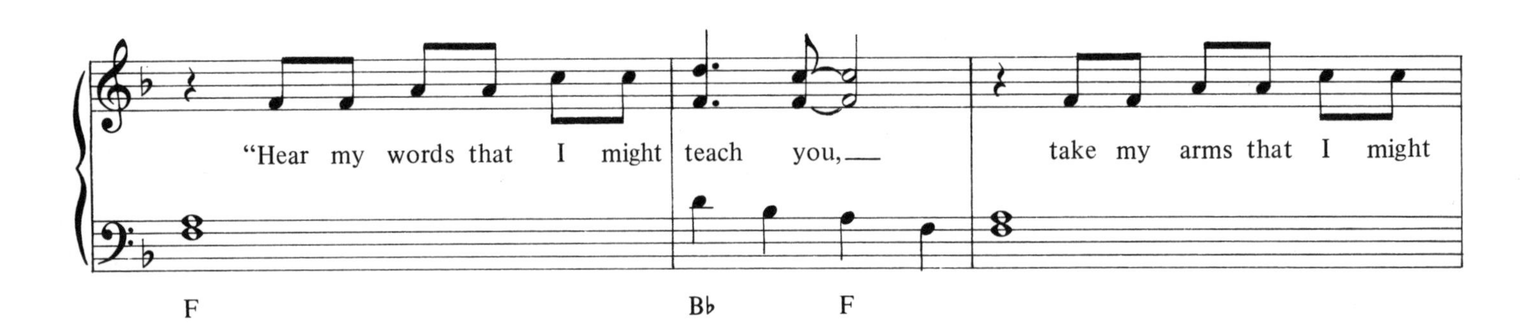
"Hear my words that I might teach you, take my arms that I might
F Bb F

reach you." But my words like si - lent rain - drops
Bb F Bb

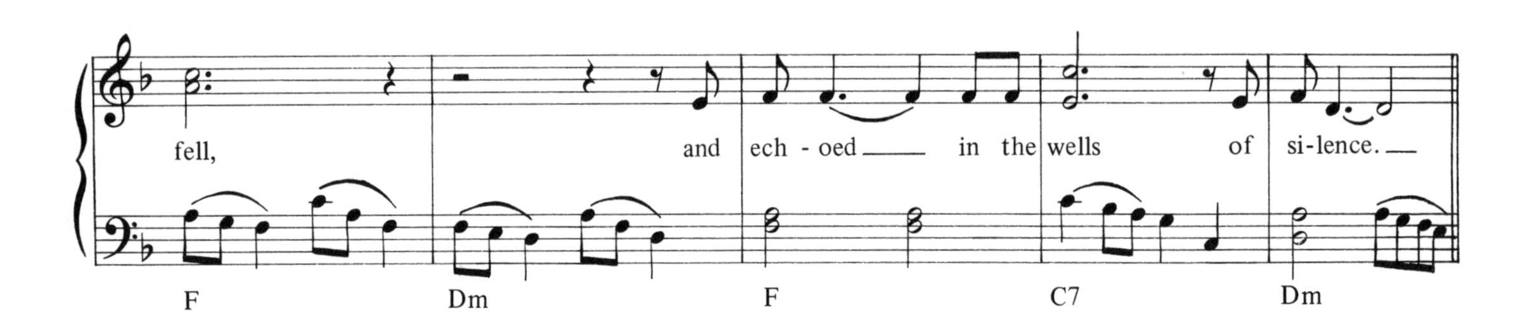
fell, and ech - oed in the wells of si-lence.
F Dm F C7 Dm

5. And the peo-ple bowed and prayed to the ne-on god they made, and the sign flashed out its warn - ing, in the words that it was form - ing. And the sign said "The words of the pro-phets are writ-ten on the sub-way walls and ten-e-ment halls," and whis-pered in the sounds of si-lence.
C
Dm
F
Bb
F
Bb
F
Bb
F
Dm
F
C7
Dm
rall.

Cecilia

Words and Music by Paul Simon

cil - ia, up in my bed - room,
I got up to wash my face, when I
F C7 F Bb

come back to bed some - one's tak - en my place.
Cel - ia, you're
F C7 F

break - ing my heart, you're shak - ing my con - fid-ence dai - ly.
Oh, Ce-
Bb F Bb F C7

cil - ia, I'm down on my knees, I'm beg - ging you please to come home
Bb F Bb F Bb F

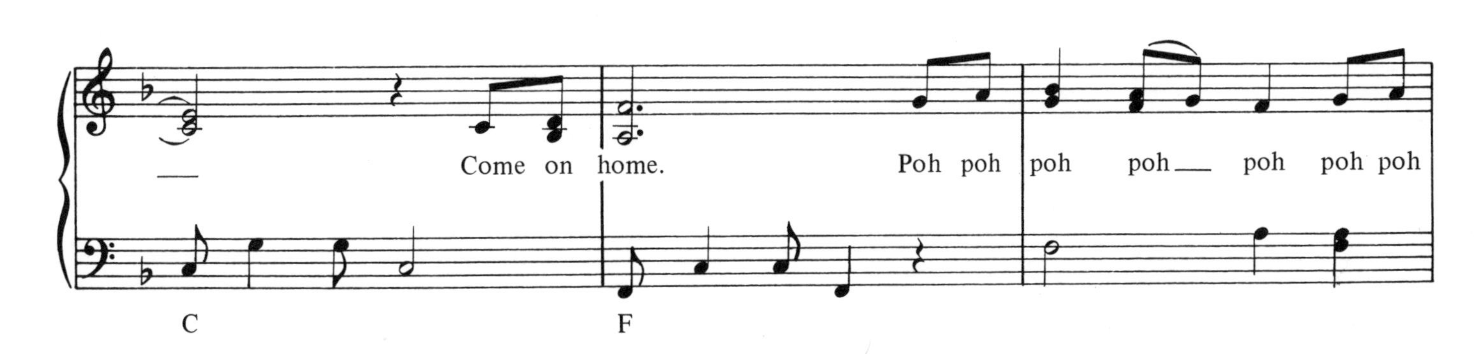
Come on home. Poh poh poh poh poh poh poh
C F

poh poh poh poh poh poh. Ju-bi-la-tion, she loves me a-gain, I
Bb C7 Bb F Bb F

fall on the floor and I laugh-ing. Ju-bi-la-tion, she loves me a-gain, I
Bb F C7 Bb F Bb F

fall on the floor and I laugh-ing. Oh oh oh oh oh oh oh oh oh oh
Bb F C7 Bb F Bb F

oh oh oh oh oh oh oh oh. Oh oh oh oh oh oh oh oh oh oh
Bb F C7 Bb F Bb F

rall.
oh oh oh oh oh oh oh oh. Come on home.
Bb F C7 F

Me And Julio Down By The Schoolyard

Words and Music by Paul Simon

saw, it was a - gainst the law. The
D G
ma - ma looked down and spit on the ground ev - 'ry time my name gets
coup-le of days they came and take me a - way, but the press let the sto - ry
G
men - tioned. The pa - pa said "Oy, if I get that boy I'm gon - na
leak. And when the rad - ic - al priest come to get me re-leased we's
C D
stick him in the house of de - ten - tion."
all on the cov - er of News - week.
Well, I'm on my
C G
way, I don't know where I'm go - ing, I'm on my
C G

way, I'm tak - ing my time but I don't know where. Good - bye
C G A7 D7
Ro - sie, the Queen of Co - ro - na, See you,
C F G
me and Ju - lio down by the school - yard. See you,
G F C D G C G
me and Ju - lio down by the school - yard. 1. In a 2. See you,
F C D G C G
me and Ju - lio down by the school - yard.
G F C D G C G

Bridge Over Troubled Water

Words and Music by Paul Simon

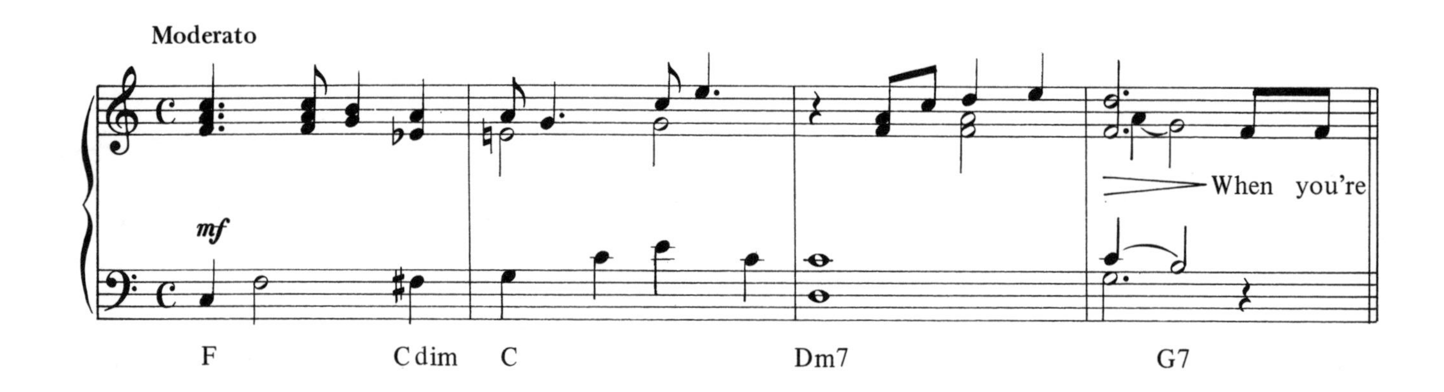

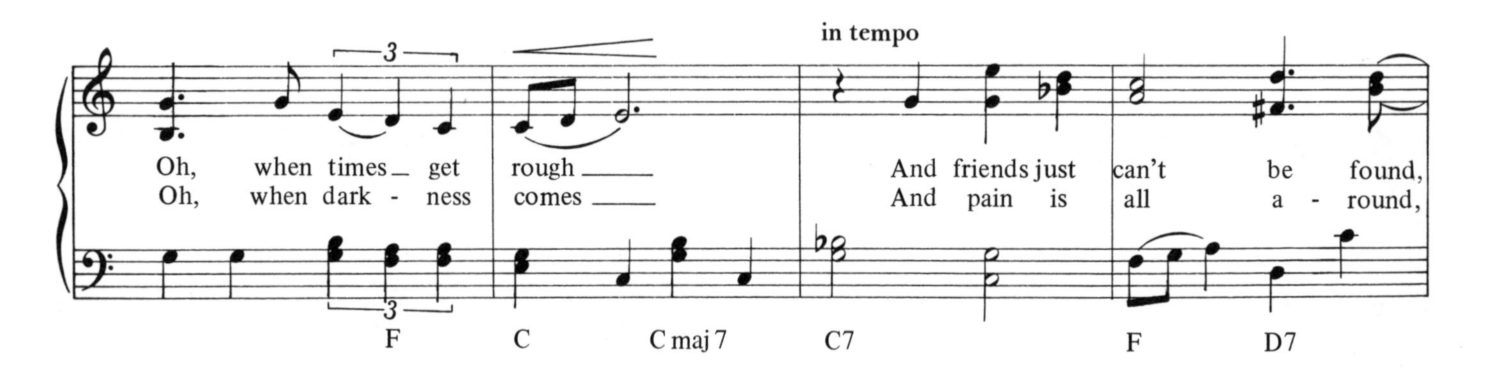

Like a bridge o - ver troub-led wa-ter, I will lay me
G C7 F C dim C A7 F E7
down. Like a bridge o - ver troub - led wa - ter, I will lay me
Am C7 F C dim C A7 F G7
1
tempo rubato
down. When you're
C F C F
2
troub - led wa - ter, I will lay me down. Sail on
C Am F Am E7 Am F
sil - ver girl, sail on by. Your time has come to shine.
C F C F B♭ F C

3
All your dreams are on their way.
See how they
F C F C F C G Am

shine.
Oh, if you need a friend,
I'm sail - ing
G G7 C C7

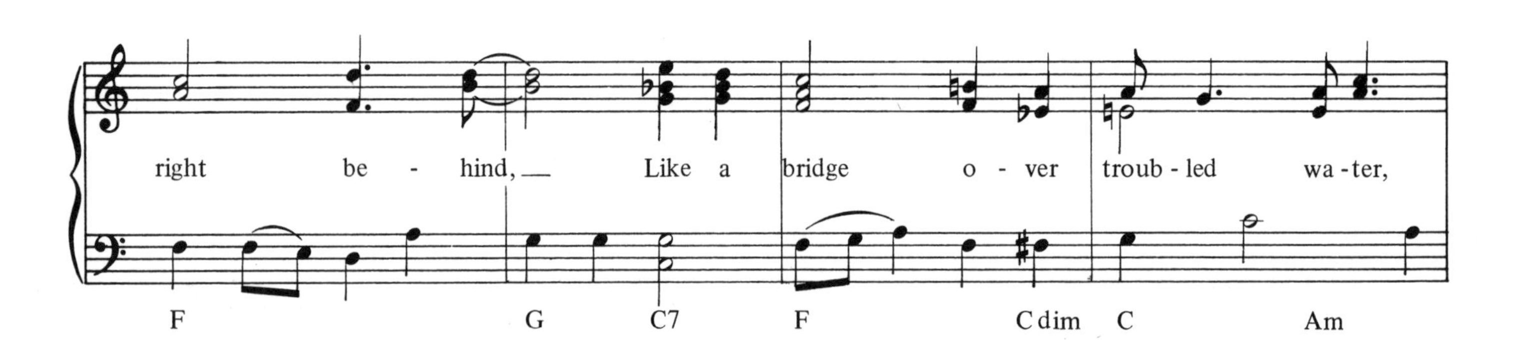
right be - hind, Like a bridge o - ver troub - led wa - ter,
F G C7 F C dim C Am

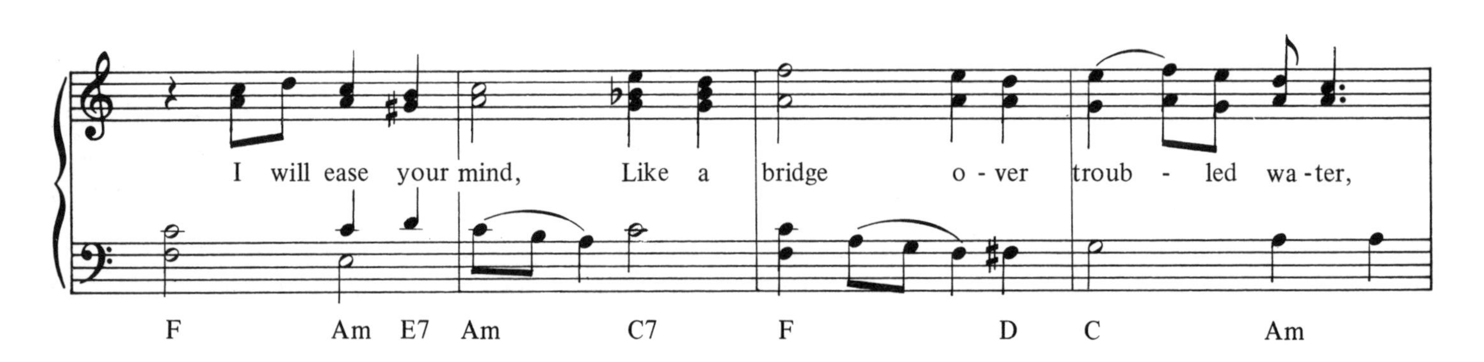
I will ease your mind, Like a bridge o - ver troub - led wa - ter,
F Am E7 Am C7 F D C Am

I will ease your mind.
F E7 Am D7 G C F C

Why Don't You Write Me

Words and Music by Paul Simon

can't make the cost of the air - fare. (Oo) Tell me
Am Em C

why, tell me why,
F Am F G

Why don't you write me? A let - ter would bright - en my love - li - est eve-ning
C D7

Mail it to-day if it's on-ly to say that you're leav - ing me. (Oo)
G7 Am Em

La la la
C F C C7

Mon-day morn-ing, sit-ting in the sun,
Hop-ing and wish-ing for the mail to come.
F7
Tues-day, nev-er got a word,
Mmm.
Wednes-day, Thurs-day, ain't no sign,
C
C7
F7
Drank a half a bottle of i-o-dine.
Fri-day, woe is me, I'm
gon-na hang my bo-dy from the
C
C7
high-est tree.
Why don't you write me?
Why don't you
F
C
C7
Repeat and fade
write me,
Why don't you write me?
Why don't you
F
F7
C
C7

The 59th Street Bridge Song (Feelin' Groovy)

Words and Music by Paul Simon

Doo-tin' doo-doo, feel - in' groo - vy. Got
F C Dm7 C F C Dm7 C
no deeds to do, no pro - mis - es to keep. I'm dap - pled and drow - sy and
F C Dm7 C F C
rea - dy to sleep. Let the morn - ing - time drop all its pet - als on me.
Dm7 C F C Dm7 C
Life, I love you, all is groo - vy.
F C Dm7 C F C Dm7 C
Repeat and fade
F C Dm7 C F C Dm7 C

The Boxer

Words and Music by Paul Simon

left my home and my fam - i - ly, I was no more than a boy, in the
C
Am
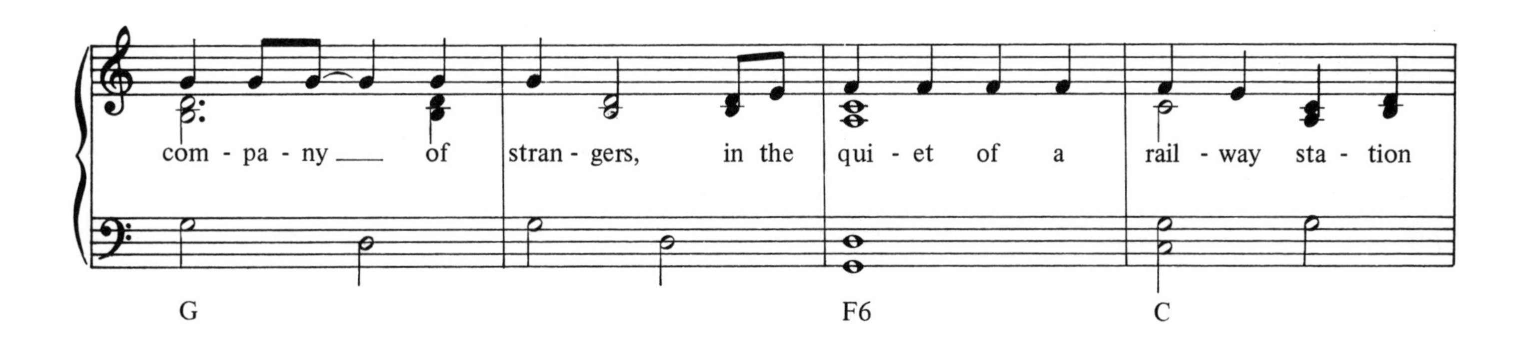
com - pa - ny of stran - gers, in the qui - et of a rail - way sta - tion
G
F6
C

run - ning scared. Lay - ing low, seek - ing
Am
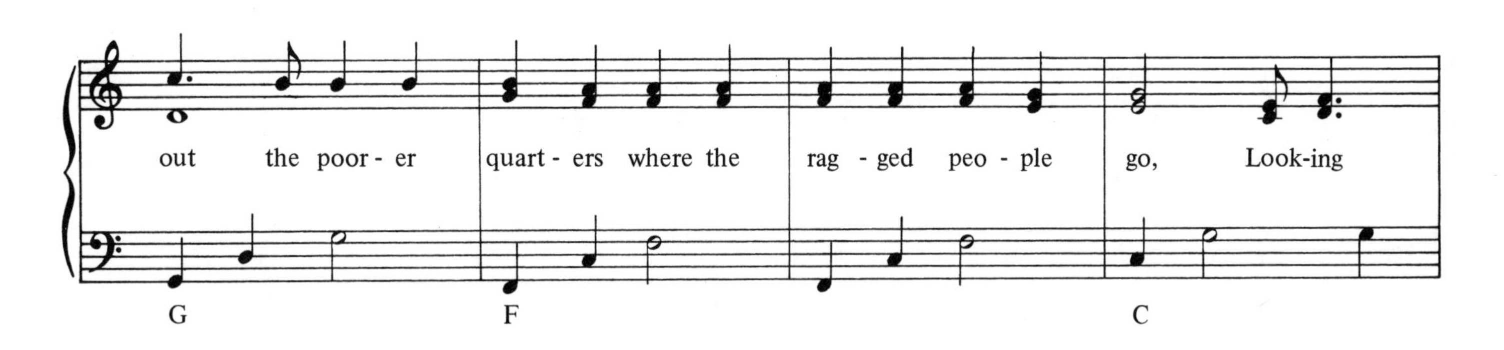
out the poor - er quart - ers where the rag - ged peo - ple go, Look-ing
G
F
C

for the pla - ces on - ly they would know. Lie - la
G
Dm
G7
C
F6
C

lie, Lei - la - lie la lie - la - lie lie - la - lie.
Am G Am
Lie - la - lie la la la la lie, la la la la lie. Ask-ing
F C F C F6 C F6
on - ly work-man's wag - es, I come look-ing for a job, but I get no of - fers.
C Am G
Just a come-on from the whores on Sev-enth Av - e - nue.
Dm C
I do de - clare, there were times when I was so lone-some, I
Am G F

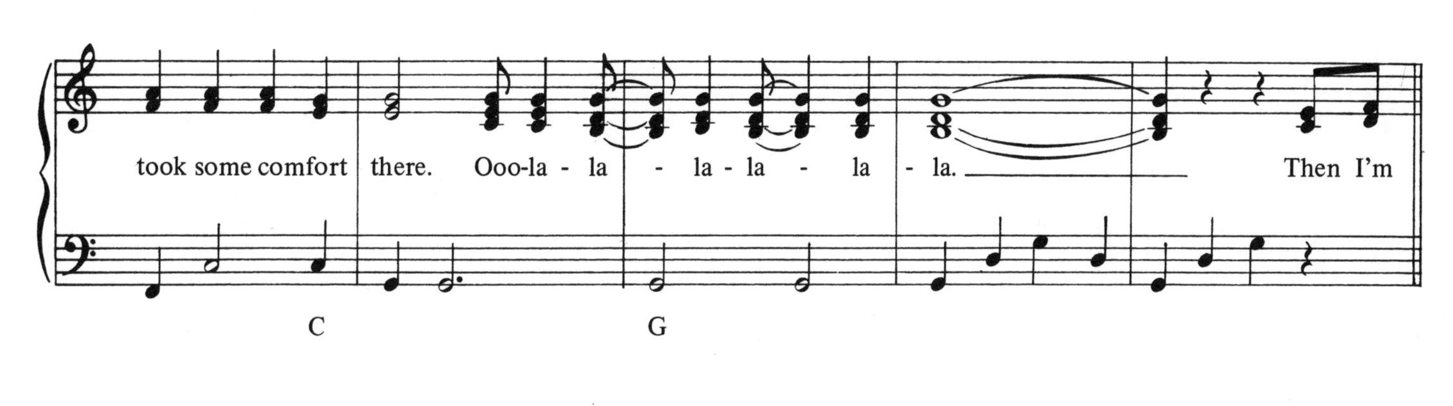
took some comfort there. Ooo-la - la - la - la - la - la. Then I'm
C G

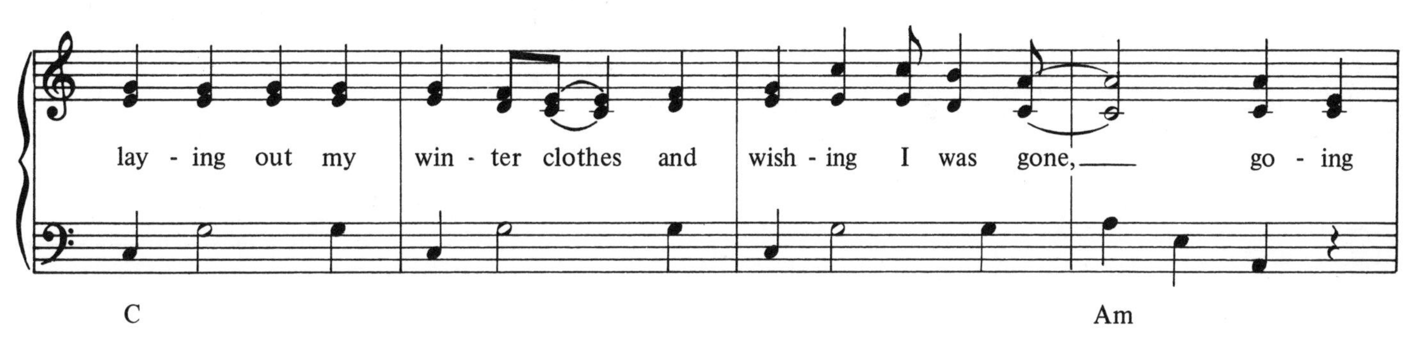
lay - ing out my win - ter clothes and wish - ing I was gone, go - ing
C Am

home, Where the New York Ci - ty win - ters are - n't
G Dm G7 C

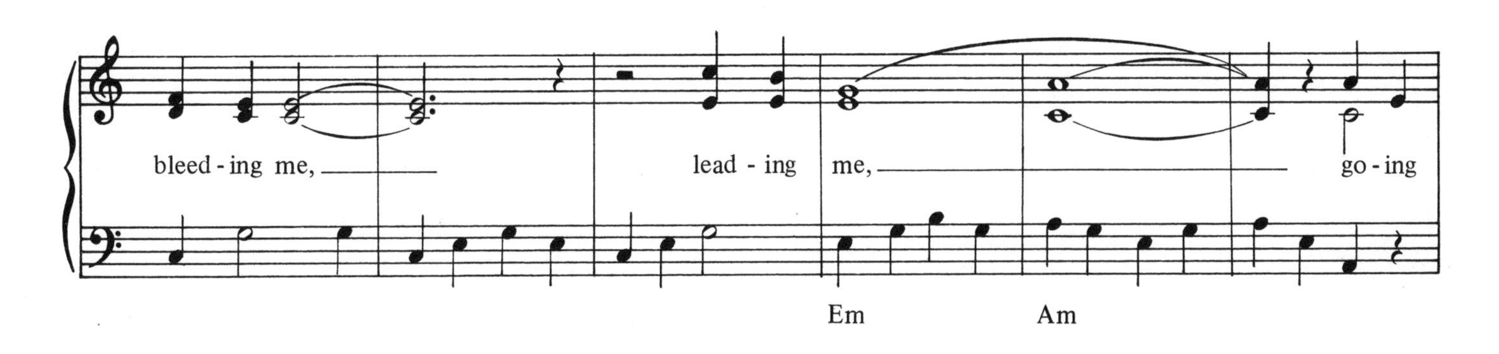
bleed - ing me, lead - ing me, go - ing
Em Am

home. In the clear - ing stands a box - er, and a fight - er by his
G C

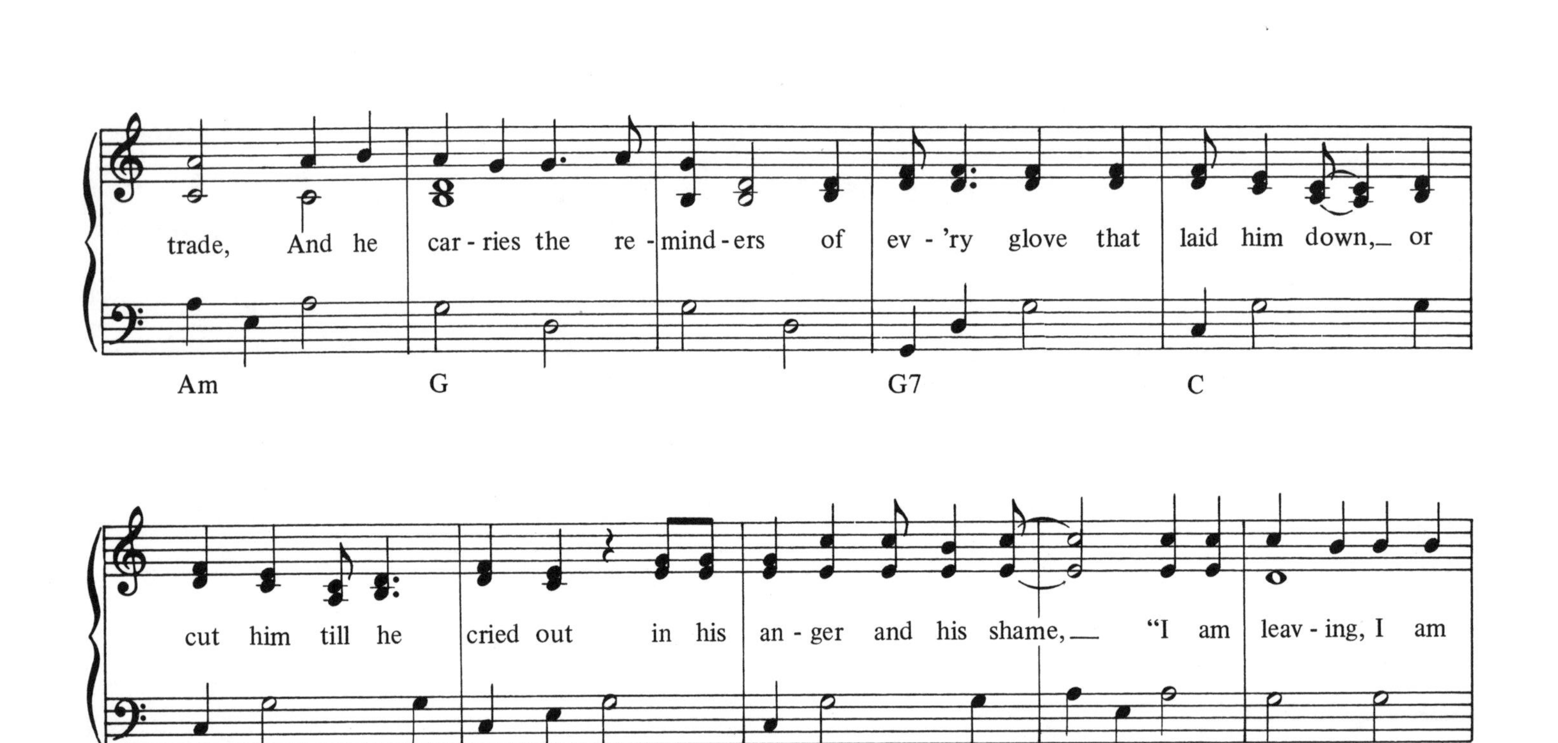
trade, And he car - ries the re - mind - ers of ev - 'ry glove that laid him down,_ or
Am G G7 C
cut him till he cried out in his an - ger and his shame,_ "I am leav - ing, I am
Am G

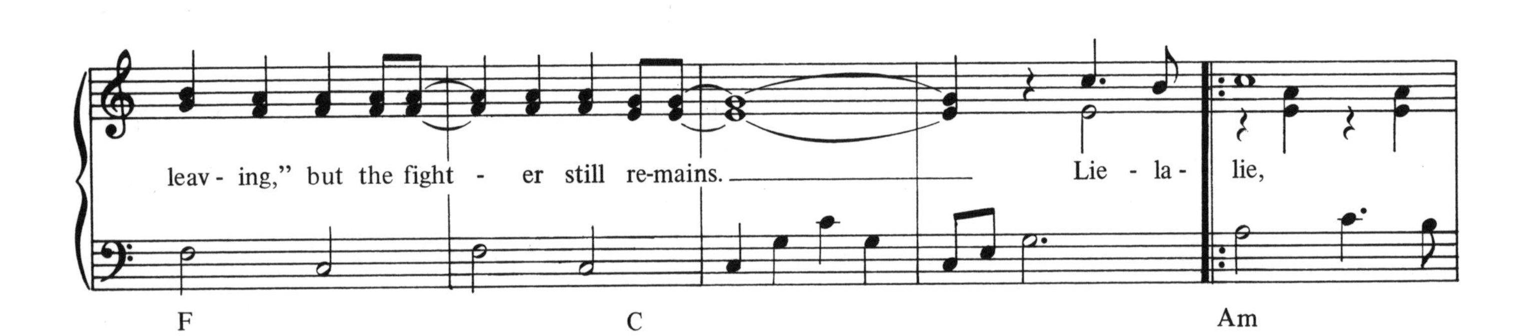
leav - ing," but the fight - er still re-mains._ Lie - la - lie,
F C Am

Lei - la - lie la lie - la - lie lie - la - lie. Lie - la -
G Am

Repeat and fade
- lie la la la la lie,_ la la la la lie._ Lie - la -
F C F C F6 C